Help with Homework
Spelling

Illustrated by
Denise Elliott

Designed and produced by
Autumn Publishing Ltd
Chichester, West Sussex

© 1999 Autumn Publishing Ltd

Printed in Spain

ISBN 1 85997 334 5

BYEWAY
B O O K S

First letter sounds

Find the stickers and put them in place. Starting with **a**, work through the alphabet and write the first letters to spell these words.

__nt

__us

__at

__uck

__gg

__ish

__oat

__at

__nk

__ug

__ite

__amb

__oon   __est   __ctopus

__enguin   __ueen   __ose

__un   __iger   __mbrella

__ase   __eb   __-ray

__o-yo   __ebra

Last letter sounds

Find the stickers and put them in place.
Look at the picture with each word and write the last letter.

cra__

be__

lea__

ba__

ca__

snai__

ja__

he__

cherr__

zi__

ca__

bo__

Last letter sounds

Look at the pictures and the words under them.

ink　　　　yacht　　　　train

sheep　　　　clown　　　　bell

How many words end with **n**? Write them on the line.

_____

How many words end with **p**? Write them on the line.

_____

How many words end with **k**? Write them on the line.

_____

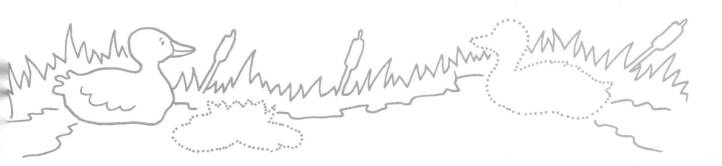

What's gone wrong?

Find the stickers and put them in place. Look carefully at this picture.
There are 10 things wrong – can you see them?

Which pet?

Find the stickers and put them in place.
Follow the leads to find out which pet each child has.

Words with a

Find the stickers and put them in place. Look at the pictures and the words under them.
Add the letter **a** to complete the words in the box.

van   cap   baby   jam   lamp

apple   hat   cat   fan   pan

_pple   c_p   c__t

h__t   b_by   l_mp

Words with e

Find the stickers and put them in place. Look at the pictures and the words under them.
Add the letter **e** to complete the words in the box.

nest   tent   hen   bell   teddy

peg   bed   vest   egg   pen

t_nt   h_n   t_ddy

_gg   p_n   b_d

Words with i

Find the stickers and put them in place.
Look at the pictures then add the letter **i** to complete these words.

pin   king   hill   zip   kitten

z_p   k_ng   k_tten

Words with o

Find the stickers and put them in place.
Look at the pictures then add the letter o to complete these words.

fox   doll   dog   cot   top

f_x   d_g   d_ll

Words with u

Find the stickers and put them in place.
Look at the pictures then add the letter **u** to complete these words.

cup   umbrella   sun   puppy

p_ppy   c_p   _mbrella

Words with a e i o u

Find the stickers and put them in place. The letters **a e i o** and **u** are called vowels.
All the other letters in the alphabet are called consonants. Look at the pictures then
add the letters **a e i o** or **u** to complete the words.
Write the words on the lines underneath.

b_by

_gg

k_tten

d_ll

p_ppy

Something beginning with s

Find the stickers and put them in place.

How many things can you see in the picture that begin with the letter **s**?

Match the words

Some words in the balloons are the same, and some look the same.
Draw lines to match the words that are the same. Then colour the balloons.

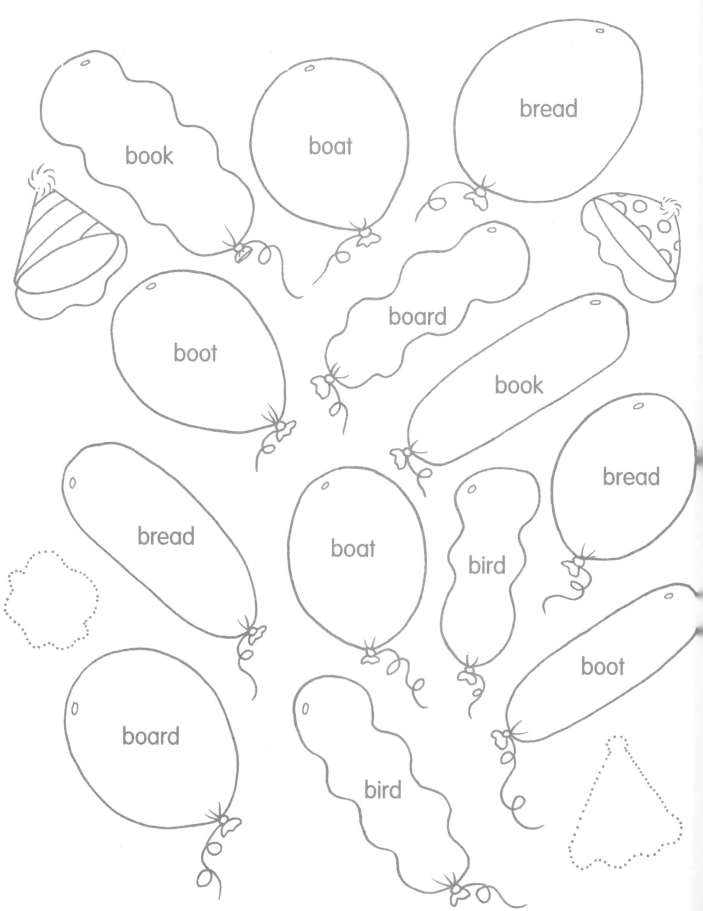

The sound ou and ow

The sound that **ou** and **ow** make is sometimes the same.
Match the words that sound the same by colouring them the same colour.

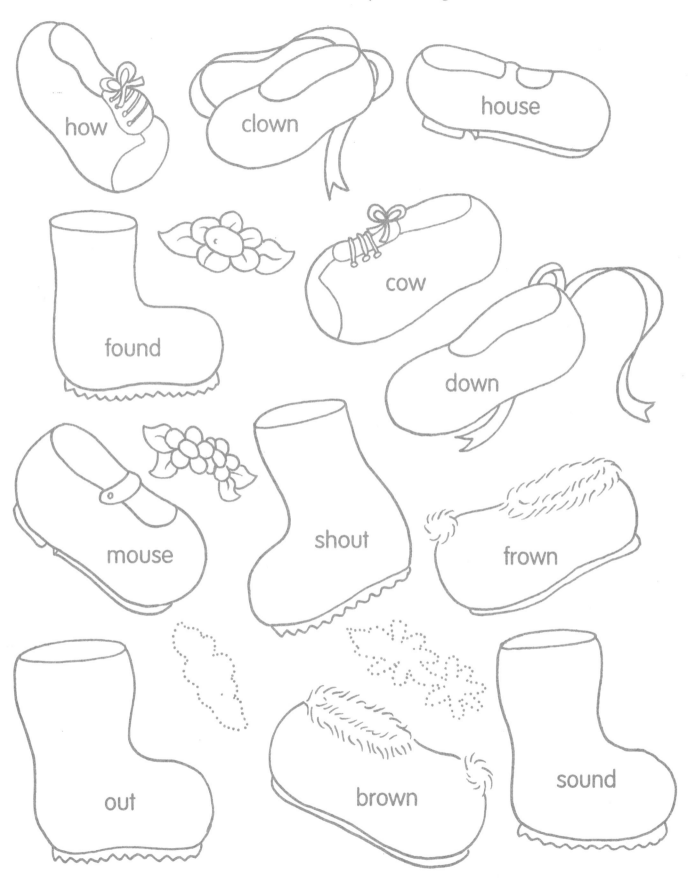

how

clown

house

found

cow

down

mouse

shout

frown

out

brown

sound

Adding e

The letter **e** at the end of a word changes the sound of the vowel.
Look at the example, then add an **e** to the words.

Example:

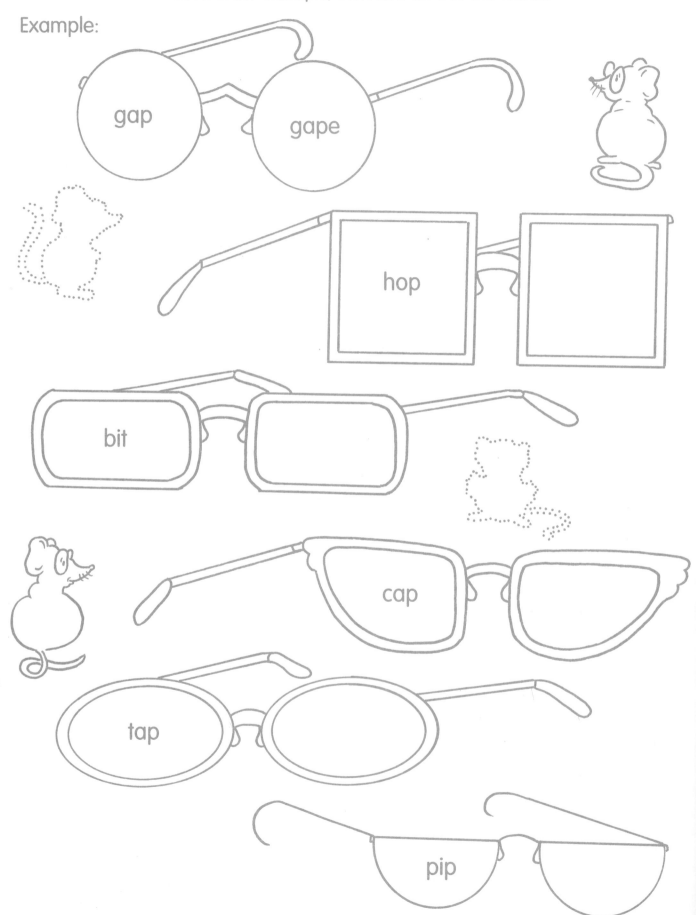

gap   gape

hop

bit

cap

tap

pip

Double letters

Find the stickers and put them in place. Find the double letters in the grid.
Look at the pictures then fill in the right double letters to complete the words.

Example:

book

f___t

br___m

dre___

ca___ot

pu___y

bu___les

| oo |
| ee |
| ss |
| rr |
| pp |
| bb |

Groups of letters

Some groups of letters make words that sound the same but are spelt differently.
Look at the words on the roof of the house and write them in the correct windows.

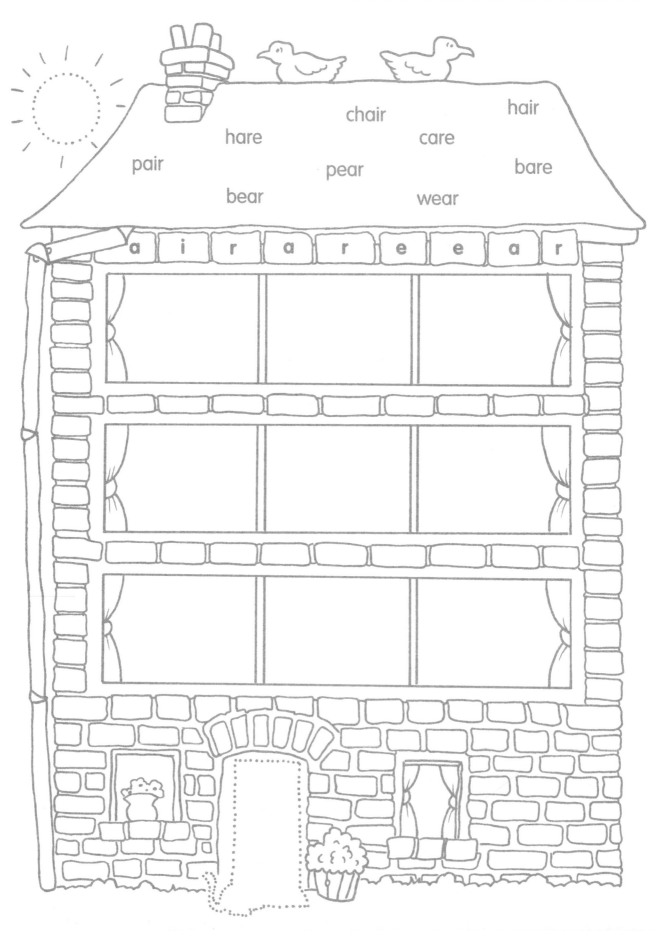

chair   hair

hare   care

pair   pear   bare

bear   wear

a i r   a i r   a r e   e e r   e a r

Word ladders

Look at the words in these ladders.
Put a tick beside the ones that you think are spelt the right way.

shoping

shopping

leaves

leeves

swimming

swiming

noyse

noise

calendar

calender

potatoe

potato

samwitch

sandwich

Seasons

Find the stickers and put them in place.

Spring

How many things begin with **r**?

Summer

How many things begin with **s**?

Autumn

How many things begin with **b**?

Winter

How many things begin with **c**?

Crossword

Find the stickers and put them in place. To do the crossword, follow the numbers across or down and fill in the words. The pictures are clues.

Animals

Find the stickers and put them in place.
Fill in the missing letters for the names of these animals.

el_ph__t

rh_n_ce_os

ebr

o_t___ch

t__er

cr_c_di__

Wordsearch

Find the stickers and put them in place. Look for the names of fruit in the wordsearch grid. You will find them by reading across or down. Draw a ring around each word. The pictures are clues.

X S R A S O H T M
W Z B P T C D F Y
X T A R R E A X P
P I N E A P P L E
Z P A U W I P M A
L I N O B C L O R
E U A H E X E K E
M G I Y R O D U W
O C H G R A P E S
N T E O Y Y N V A

Adding s or es

When you have more than one of something this is called a plural.
Some plurals can be spelt by adding **s**, and some by adding **es**.
Look at the list and make these words into plurals.

plurals with s	plurals with es
shop	bus
pear	dish
spider	bunch
piano	fox
horse	potato
hand	witch
light	tomato

Hidden words

The words in the cups have a word hidden in them.
Draw a line under the word. Look at the example.

Example:

done
bones
gone
phone

wanted
elephants
plants
chant

wander
sandal
candle
grandad

Fruit

Find the stickers and put them in place. Fill in the missing letters to spell the names of the fruit.

ap_ _e

pe_ _h

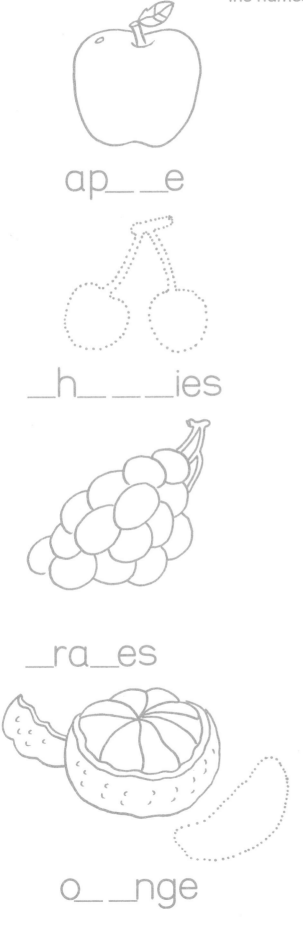

_h_ _ _ies

ba_ _n_

_ra_es

me_on

o_ _nge

_e_r

Letters s or z

In some words the letter **s** sounds like **z**. Look at the words in the big kite. Write the words that sound like **s** in one of the smaller kites and the words that sound like **z** in the other.

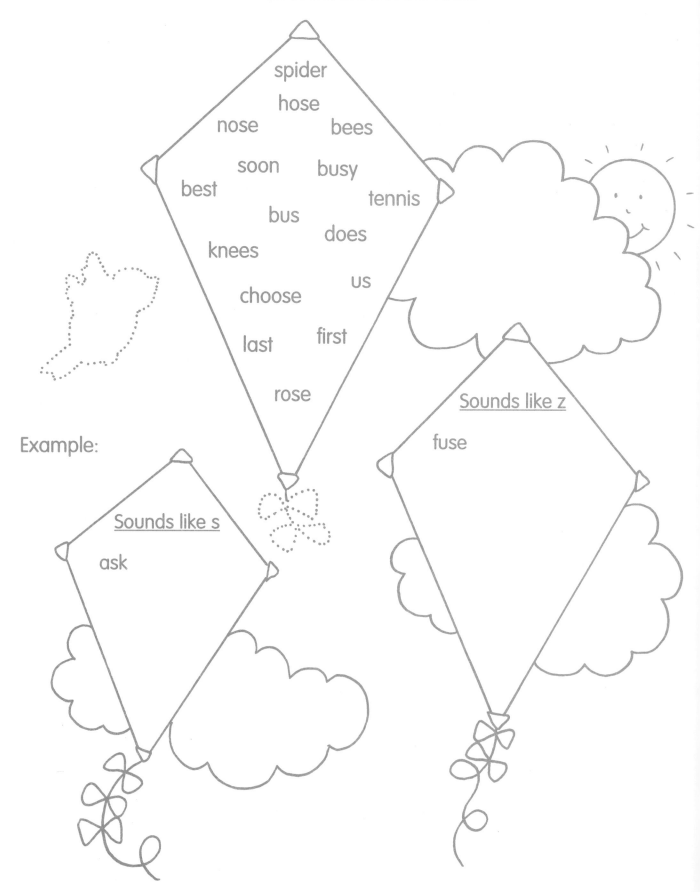

spider
hose
nose   bees
soon   busy
best   tennis
bus
does
knees
choose   us
last   first
rose

Example:

Sounds like z
fuse

Sounds like s
ask

Match the words

Draw lines to match the words that look and sound similar.

flower

wish

box

hand

parrot

fish

shower

carrot

fox

drain

train

land

Answers

Last letter sounds
How many words end with **n** ? 2 - train and clown
How many words end with **p** ? 1 - sheep
How many words end with **k** ? 1 - ink

What's gone wrong?
1 pig in the sky
2 flowers in chimney
3 cakes in tree
4 dinosaur on a lead
5 duck cleaning with a broom
6 rain cloud on grass
7 hen wearing a hat
8 shark fin in pond
9 sheep wearing trainers
10 girl wearing only one boot

Something beginning with s
sun, sailing boat, surf board, sandcastle, spade,
sandals, shells, sea, sand, starfish, seagull,
sunglasses, seaweed, swimming costume, sky,
shorts, sunhat, surfers
.... can you see anymore?

Adding e
cape   hope   tape
bite   pipe

Groups of letters

<u>air</u>	<u>are</u>	<u>ear</u>
chair	bare	pear
pair	hare	bear
hair	care	wear

Word ladders
shopping
leaves
swimming
noise
calendar
potato
sandwich

Seasons
r - rainbow, rabbits, roller skates, rain
s - sun, sausages, straws, sandwiches,
       salad, shoes
b - bonfire, ball, boots, bobble hat, barrel
c - cat, cactus, crayons, curtains, colouring
       ...can you see anymore?

Crossword

Animals
elephant   tiger   rhinoceros
zebra   ostrich   crocodile

Wordsearch

Adding s or es
shops   buses
pears   dishes
spiders   bunches
pianos   foxes
horses   potatoes
hands   witches
lights   tomatoes

Hidden words
one   ant   and

Fruit
apple peach cherries banana
grapes melon orange pear

Letter s or z

<u>Sounds like s</u>	<u>Sounds like z</u>
spider	nose
first	busy
last	rose
best	bees
us	does
soon	hose
bus	knees
tennis	choose

Match the words
flower/ shower   drain/ train
hand/ land   parrot/ carrot
box/ fox   wish/ dish